21/‑
7a

METHODS FOR THE EXAMINATION

OF ROOT SYSTEMS

AND ROOTS

Institute for Soil Fertility, Groningen

METHODS FOI

Methods in use at the Institute f

CENTRE FOR

AGRICULTURAL PUBLICATIONS AND DOCUMENTATION

WAGENINGEN MCMLXIV

J. J. SCHUURMAN and M. A. J. GOEDEWAAGEN

THE EXAMINATION

OF ROOT SYSTEMS

AND ROOTS

;oil Fertility for eco-morphological root investigations

*With 36 illustrations, 158 literature references and
a bibliography index*

Dr. J. J. SCHUURMAN is senior scientific officer at the Institute for Soil Fertility in Groningen and lecturer at the Agricultural University in Wageningen. Dr. M. A. J. GOEDEWAAGEN, now retired, was senior scientific officer at the same Institute.
J. J. H. DE BOER, L. KNOT and B. SCHÄFFNER, of the same Institute, have contributed considerably to the development of the methods described. They have also given valuable assistance in writing this book.

© CENTRE FOR AGRICULTURAL PUBLICATIONS AND DOCUMENTATION,

WAGENINGEN 1965

DESIGNED AND PRINTED IN HOLLAND BY VADA, WAGENINGEN

Contents

I. Introduction

The growth of a plant is governed by an interaction of two processes, – the formation of organic material by the green aerial parts, and the uptake of nutrients and moisture by the roots. When there is poor carbon dioxide assimilation the root growth is also adversely affected, and when the roots are only able to absorb small amounts of nutrients or moisture the aerial growth will also be impaired. This means that phenomena observed above the ground may be caused by soil factors which affect the development of the root system and consequently the absorptive capacity of the roots.

In addition to such factors as the presence of nutrients and moisture in the soil and the activity of the root system, the absorptive capacity of the latter is determined by its morphological extension. Generally speaking, it is important for all agricultural crops to have a well-developed root system as this guarantees a better crop, the plant being enabled to make use of the deeper soil layers. This enhances its resistance to the difficult periods that often occur during the vegetative period of a plant. This means that it is important for root development to be disturbed as little as possible. Consequently farmers should be aware of the factors that promote and impede root growth and know how the latter can be improved. With this knowledge a conscious effort may be made to further root growth. Experiments may be carried out for this purpose and the knowledge acquired used on a subsequent occasion when seeking to explain the phenomena observed in the aerial parts of the plant.

Root studies have an ecological aim in which either the physiological or morphological aspects may be emphasized. The present work is confined to morphological research.

The object of root study methods is to assemble data on certain characteristic morphological features of the roots.

The following properties of the root system are important for eco-morphological research:

1. *The total amount of roots.* This gives an approximate idea of the absorptive capacity of the root system, but two plants are only comparable provided they have similar root systems. This means that strictly speaking such a comparison is limited to plants of the same species. The total amount of roots is nearly always expressed in grams after the roots have been dried, but it is equally possible to calculate the total length of all roots or to measure the total surface area.

The total surface area of all roots may be regarded as an important characteristic, but it is one which is extremely difficult to calculate, and moreover not every part of the surface area is functionally similar.

In connection with the problems of supplying the soil with organic material it may also be important to calculate the total weight of roots, or the weight in the tilth only.

2. *The formation of branch roots and the diameter.* The absorptive capacity of a root system is partly determined by the degree of branching and the diameter of the roots. It is also important to calculate the root diameter in order to judge the comparability of two root systems.

3. *The vertical distribution in the profile.* It is ascertained which layers have dense root development and which less dense. From this it is possible to draw conclusions on the nutrient and the moisture uptake from these layers. This may be important for the drought resistance of a crop.

4. *The lateral distribution in the profile.* It is important to determine this in connection with such cultural practices as mechanical hoeing. The plant spacing may be related to lateral root growth.

5. *The maximum depth and width.* The maximum depth is important in connection with the problem of the depth to which the plant can still absorb nutrients and moisture from the soil. The maximum width is important in connection with the layer in which it occurs (cf. 4).

10

6. *The rate of development.* Comparison between a number of stages of growth affords an idea of the rate of growth. This may be important in connection with periods of drought or frost which may be fatal when root growth is less rapid. Rapid root growth may also be important when nutrients are washed out of the soil.

Methods of root study should aim at elucidating these problems. This research work may be carried out either in field experiments or conditioned container experiments. Both require special methods for making the roots accessible for study. To some extent the same methods can be employed, but otherwise they need to be adapted to the given conditions. The methods will be discussed in the following order:

Field experiments

The methods in use may be classified as follows:

1. *Investigation of monoliths.* This includes the pinboard method (p. 13) and the excavations. These two procedures give a fairly complete picture of the structure and shape of the root system and of the total amount of roots. This method may also throw light on the distribution of the roots in the profile and their maximum depth. It also affords possibilities of determining the rate of growth. The branching of the roots can also be determined in a pinboard specimen.

2. *Investigation of soil samples of small volume.* In this investigation use may be made of augers or similar tools (p. 31). Fragments of the root system are obtained by means of which it is possible to obtain accurate data on the amount of roots in each layer. This is also a fairly simple way of obtaining information on the vertical distribution in the profile and the maximum depth. Sampling at various distances from the plant provides information on the lateral spread of the roots, and periodical sampling may give some insight into the growth rate of the roots.

The *evaluation method* has been developed from the auger method (p. 43).

3. *Investigation of profile walls.* This includes in the first place mapping (p. 50), followed by root counts. This method is very suitable for determining the distribution of the roots in the profile and hence their maximum depth. The total amount of roots in a given site can be expressed numerically. This method is less suitable for determining root branching and growth rate. The roots can not only be mapped but loosened on the wall en masse and then drawn or photographed.

Container experiments

In these experiments plants are cultivated under predetermined conditions; this often simplifies the problem involved and the plan of the experiments (p. 58).

Use is made of cylinders, cases or glass-panelled boxes filled with soil, and water cultures in glass cylinders, or else combinations of these containers.

II. Field experiments

1. Monolith investigation - The pinboard method

Material

ROTMISTROFF (1908) applied this method to plants grown in boxes. MASCHHAUPT (1915) was the first to apply it to a crop in the field. Later on it was used by GOEDEWAAGEN for box cultures and in the field. Use is made of a board of given dimensions in which pins are fastened (Fig. 1). These pins are cut-off knitting needles. For driving the needles into the board use is

FIG. 1.
Pinboards of various sizes

made of a small tube of which the length is equal to the required needle length. This tube is provided with a base. The tube prevents the needles from buckling as they are driven into the wood. The needles are arranged in a pattern of squares 5 cm apart.

The dimensions of the pinboards and length of the needles are adjusted to the plants which have to be sampled, so that pinboards are used of various dimensions and needle length. The most common sizes are height 1 metre, width 30 cm, needle length 8 cm, and height 1 metre, width 60 cm, needle length 14 cm. The first type is generally used for research on plants which have narrow root systems, e.g. those found in pastures, and the second for crops with broad, extensive root systems, e.g. potatoes, beets, colza, etc. Before a pinboard sample is taken, a sheet of black plastic material is stretched out on the board and pressed between the needles until it rests on the board. A lath may be used for this purpose. The advantage of using the plastic sheet is that after the soil has been washed off and the rinsings have disappeared the root system can be readily removed from the board intact.

Sampling

When the pinboard is ready for use, plant observations are made. Notes are made on the stand, state of development and any weed growth. A site is then selected where the crop appears to be representative of the field concerned. A hole about a metre square is dug next to this site, after which the wall facing the plant or plants is cut vertically and levelled off.

When plants are cultivated in rows the wall can be dug either parellel to the row or at right angles to it. In the first case the specimen will contain a part of a single row which is of the same width as the pinboard, and in the second plants are obtained from two or more rows provided the board is wide enough. In the second case it is possible to study to what extent root development differs below the plants and between the rows, and how far the roots of a plant extend laterally. In the first case the distance from the wall to the plant or plants will be a few inches, so that the plants will be situated approximately in the centre of the specimen or slightly above. A description is then made of the profile together with all data that may be important for the interpretation of the root pattern, e.g. type of soil, water table or height of the site above the ditch-water level, and the thickness and characteristics of the tilth and subsoil.

A calculation is made of the force required to drive a conical object into the various soil layers. A penetrometer can be used for this purpose. It has been found that this force increases with a constant weight by volume and decreasing moisture content, and also with an increasing weight by volume and a constant moisture content (SCHUURMAN, unpublished). A model form is used for noting these observations. If necessary soil samples may be taken to the laboratory. A number of preliminary observations are also made on the width and depth of the root zone. For this purpose use is made of a coarse needle (sack needle) the eye of which is fixed to a handle, or else a three-pronged garden scraper. These operations over, the plank is held in a vertical position and the needle points pressed horizontally against the wall so that the top row of needles is exactly level with the surface. When the surface is uneven the highest point is selected. The needles are then driven into the soil by means of a jack-screw or by striking the back of the board with a mallet. Once the board has been forced against the wall a horizontal trench is dug underneath it to a depth of a few inches more than the length of the needles. The board is then supported by means of a jackscrew (Fig. 2). Vertical trenches are then dug on either side of the board, these also being a few inches deeper than the length of the needles.

A twisted steel rope with a handle at each end is then placed in these trenches. The maximum thickness of the rope is 2 mm. The pinboard specimen is sawn loose from the soil by making sawing movements with this steel rope, after which the specimen

Fig. 2. *Pinboard in the soil,*
supported by a jackscrew

is pulled backward so that it lies horizontally in the hole. The soil is now held on the pinboard by the pins. Depending on the size and weight of the specimen, it can be lifted out of the hole by two or four persons, if necessary with the help of ropes. For heavy boards, however, a better method is that in which use is made of ropes fitted with tackle hooks. These hooks can be fastened to the underside, and this should be done before the specimen is sawn off with the steel rope. Two smooth beams should be laid in the trench at the same time in an oblique position from the underside of the board and ascending to the surface on the opposite side of the hole. The heavy specimen can then be easily hauled over these beams by means of the rope (for instance, by means of a car). To prevent the specimen from breaking it is wrapped in a sack. It is then ready to be taken to the laboratory.

16

For certain purposes horizontal pinboard specimens are sometimes taken. In this case the above ground parts of the plant should first be harvested. Before a specimen is taken some slight levelling of the surface is occasionally required, after which the needles on the board are pressed into the profile from above. The soil is then dug away round the board and a wooden box is then fitted round the pinboard and the specimen. There is a groove on the bottom of the box, below the needles. A steel plate having a projecting point and a cutting edge is forced through these grooves and underneath the specimen by means of a jack-screw. Once the specimen has been cut loose it can be lifted out as it rests on the metal plate, after which the next layer can be sampled. To prevent the specimen from being pushed away when the plate is inserted it should be supported at the rear.

Washing the specimen

If the soil is sand or loamy sand the specimen is placed in a wooden washing vessel in the laboratory without previous treatment. The inside dimensions of this vessel are length 130 cm, width 80 cm and depth 35 cm. The vessel is slightly inclined, its lower side facing a gutter. Holes drilled in this lower side can be opened or closed at will by means of corks. After the soil specimen has been placed in the vessel the latter is filled with water. The entire clod is kept immersed until the soil is considered to be saturated. This greatly reduces the risk of clods breaking off and roots being lost. An initial soaking period of from 12-24 hours is usually sufficient. Washing can then be begun.

The specimen should be washed with particular care when the water level in the vessel during washing is always slightly below the top of the pinboard specimen. But this is not always strictly necessary. The washing can be carried out by one person with the help of a sprinkler, but this has the drawback that in most cases the pressure is not kept constant, especially when

FIG. 3. *Rotary sprinkler above a pinboard specimen*

layers of varying hardness occur in the profile. As a result the specimen may be damaged, and it is therefore better to wash a specimen mechanically. This can be done with the rotary sprinkler having three arms about 17 cm long in which is perforated a row of small holes (Fig. 3). Owing to the slightly oblique position of these holes the sprinkler is rotated by the pressure of the water. The advantage of this is that the drops do not always fall on the same place but are distributed over the entire trajectory. This method has several advantages. In the first place better results are obtained because all material is washed with the same force, and secondly a larger number of profiles can be washed at the same time, only one person being required for continuous supervision. Such contaminations as straws, pieces of stalk or leaves in the soil should be removed during washing before they become entangled in the root mass. Provided the sprinkler is properly supervised the amount of water consumed need not exceed that used when a specimen is washed by one person with a watering sprayer. Washing should not be too vigorous as this may damage the roots, and cut-off

18

FIG. 4. *Oscillating sprinkler above a pinboard specimen*

roots from plants outside the specimen may be washed away.

The specimen may also be mechanically washed by means of a specially modified garden sprinkler of which the spray nozzle is moved to and fro by the force of the water. This sprinkler cleans a rectangular area of the specimen (Fig. 4). This is an improvement on the rotating apparatus. The size of this area depends on the distance from the spray nozzle to the specimen and the length of the spray nozzle. In favourable cases a pinboard specimen size 60 x 100 cm can be washed in a single operation. The trajectory can be adjusted to three positions. The apparatus also has about the same advantages as the rotary sprinkler. It can moreover be used when it is desired to compare the hardness of the layers in similar profiles, since a part of both profiles can be washed simultaneously and hence with the same force.

It is far more difficult to wash pinboard samples of heavy clay, and very heavy clay specimens are even practically impossible to wash without making special provisions. In this case it is useless to wash the specimen with water. Attempts have been made to use a motor pump for washing with water in which a peptising material was dissolved. The water was pumped from a tank, sprayed on the specimen, then returned to the tank and used again, and so on. One solution used was sodium pyrophosphate. But this experiment was unsuccessful. In some cases fairly good results have been obtained by drying the entire specimen at 100° C and then immersing it in a sodium pyrophosphate solution. Owing to the drying of the specimen the solution can penetrate quickly and be more uniformly dispersed in the specimen. The concentration of the solution is usually 270 grams of sodium pyrophosphate to 100 litres of water, but for very heavy clay the concentration should be increased. Drying should not be so extensive as to cause large cracks, as in this case the roots will break. After the specimen has lain in the solution for about 12 hours an attempt can be made to wash it in the usual way. Should this not be fully possible (it depends on the degree of penetration of the sodium pyrophosphate) the process may be repeated. We are still investigating whether freezing of the specimen may have a good effect on the washability. Some favourable indications have already been obtained.

Final steps

After the specimen has been cleaned the pinboard and roots are transferred to a flat zinc basin of water, and the specimen can then be profiled and cleaning continued. In these two processes loose roots twisted round the needles are restored to their original position and any contaminations still present, e.g. straws, etc., are removed. The cleaning can be carried out, at least in part, by filling the basin with water and then passing through it a thin stream of water which runs over the edge.

After the specimen has been washed and arranged the root system can be photographed as it lies on the pinboard in the water. The advantage of photographing under water is that the natural position of the finer roots is also preserved. The black

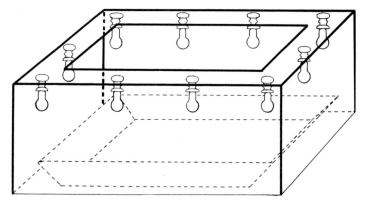

Fig. 5. *Wooden case with bulbs, used for photographing a root system*

plastic sheet takes a good background. For lighting use may be made of a box in which is arranged a number of bulbs, enabling the roots to be uniformly illuminated (Fig. 5); there is no possibility of light being reflected on to the lens via the surface of the water. Since the photograph is taken vertically the reflecting parts of the camera should be blackened in order to prevent it from being reflected in the water. Ceiling reflection can be prevented in the same way. Instead of a box use may be made of four powerful "fotomirenta" bulbs arranged round the basin in such a way as to give a good distribution of the light and prevent it from being reflected in the lens. Figure 6 shows a root system being photographed under water. Figure 7 shows the same root system being photographed under water after it had been removed from the pinboard by means of the plastic underlayer.

The roots can also be photographed dry after arranging. In this case the water is carefully siphoned out of the basin until the roots are free of the water. The root system is then dried with a fan until the outside is practically air-dry. It is then removed from the pinboard by carefully lifting the plastic sheet between the needles. The root system can then be taken off the sheet,

21

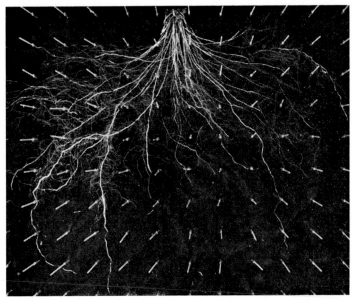

Fig. 6.   *Photograph of a submerged root system on a pinboard*

placed on black velvet or black-painted hardboard, and then photographed. Figure 8 shows the result of such a photograph.

It is clear that when the roots (at least, the roots of larger plants) are examined by means of pinboards one does not obtain an entire root system but only a vertical section of it. The roots cut off from the front and rear of the specimen are absent, and this means that the photograph only shows a certain cross-section of the root system. Despite this it provides a good indication of the root system as a whole. HUDIG (1939) more or less overcame this difficulty by taking a cube of soil on two pinboards size 30 x 30 cm of which the needles intersected at right-angles.

In both cases, after the roots have been photographed they can be collected in layers in order to calculate the weights. In most cases, however, this is not done immediately, the first step

22

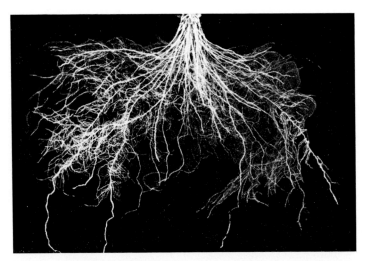

FIG. 7.   *Photograph of the submerged root system removed from the pinboard*

FIG. 8.   *Root system of figure 7, now photographed in the dried state*

23

being to describe the root system. The aerial parts of the plant in the specimen are also photographed, the distance being, as far as possible, the same as for the roots. This gives a uniform magnification of corresponding photographs.

Description of root systems and roots

The root system obtained from a pinboard has to be described. The description can be divided into one of the root system as a whole and a detailed description of one or more separate roots. A separate scheme is employed for each.

The following scheme is used for describing the root system as a whole:

A. *Description of a root system*

1. *general picture*
   a. shape (square, oblong, etc.)
   b. maximum depth in cm
   c. width in cm
   d. colour
   e. number of zones distinguished according to change in the shape of the root system or in the density of the root zone.
2. *description by zones*
   a. height in cm
   b. width in cm
   c. density of the root zone (in terms of sparse to very abundant roots)
   d. distribution of the roots over the width of the board in the soil (in terms of regular and irregular)
   e. colour.

If detailed information is required about the roots, for instance on the branching, separate roots can be placed between transparent plastic material. In this method two or more representative fully-grown roots are carefully worked loose from a root system so that they remain intact with their sideroots. This is a difficult task, but experience has shown that the method can even be successfully applied to dense root systems provided no force is used. The number of roots prepared depends, for example, on the type of investigation and the kind of root system. In the case of a plant whose roots show marked differences in growth habit (either as a result of its hereditary predisposition or external factors), one part being confined to the top soil and another growing in a distinctly vertical direction, roots have to be taken from both groups for detailed investigation. This is obviously the case with potatoes.

In the case of cereals it is possible to select either the nodal or seminal roots, or both. For studying the effect of soil factors it is useful to choose fully grown roots. The oldest roots are better avoided as they may exhibit symptoms of decay. This method also affords a good idea of the growth of the roots of a particular plant by working loose roots of different ages, viz. from young to old, and comparing them.

For this purpose the best procedure is to place the root system in a long, fairly broad and shallow basin. The bottom of the basin is preferably dark when light-coloured roots are being handled, and vice versa. The basin is filled with 4 to 5 cm of water. Since the basin is wide, any roots not used can be put on one side without being cut off at once. Generally the best procedure is to remove young unbranched roots in the first case. This makes it easier to free fully grown, densely branched roots. If there is a root which it is required to use in a completely free state it can be cut off. For the further processing of this root use is made of a long, comparatively narrow and shallow basin of which the bottom is lined with a sheet of fairly firm transparent plastic material which should have no folds or crease as it may later be necessary to take photographs or photoprints. The margins of this plastic sheet are weighted to prevent it from floating when the vessel is filled with a thin layer of water. The

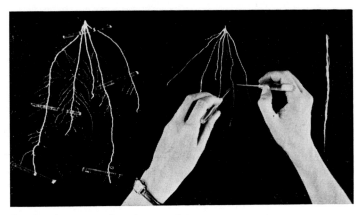

FIG. 9. *Arrangement of roots by means of pins*

moistened root is placed in this basin. The side-roots are then arranged with the help of needles (Fig. 9). It is important that only a small amount of water is used as otherwise any awkward movement may have the effect of disturbing the water and thereby entangling the roots. Fortunately when roots have only a few side-roots the water adhering to them is sufficient. When arranging the roots the usual practice is to work from the base downward. When all roots have been arranged in order, the water is carefully removed with a water-jet vacuum pump. To prevent the roots from being entrained by the water they are weighted with glass rods. The roots are then left to dry for some time, when they begin to adhere loosely to the plastic sheet. Care should be taken, however, as the roots may dry at different rates and dry roots may suddenly become detached. This can be prevented, however, by using a vaporiser for spraying the roots with a glue which is colourless after drying, viz. Saba 810 E, dissolved in water in a ratio of 1 : 5. Any excess glue can be removed with a water-jet vacuum pump. The glue takes about 30 minutes to dry, but drying can be accelerated with a fan. The roots are then stuck to the plastic sheet and show no further tendency to spring out of position. Afterwards the whole can

26

Fig. 10. *Root partly between plastic sheets*

be covered with the second sheet of thin plastic in order to protect it (Fig. 10).

A photograph can be taken of roots obtained in this way, but it is desirable to remove the thin plastic sheet beforehand as it may create a number of reflection points. The roots should then again be covered as quickly as possible with a thin sheet of plastic.

The entire process could also be carried out between glass sheets, but plastic has the advantage of being flexible, so that the entire root system can be placed in a rotating photostat camera and photoprints made. The thin plastic sheet is also removed in this process so that the light-sensitive paper comes into direct contact with the roots and a very sharp photograph is obtained of the thin roots. Roots which vary extensively in thickness make poor photoprints and are better photographed. These photoprints or photographs, which give an accurate picture of the roots, can be used afterwards for the purpose of measuring and counting.

The following descriptive scheme is employed:

B. *Description of individual roots*

   I. *Dicotyledones*
     1. *main root*
       a. shape (tap root, filiform, etc.)
       b. length in cm
       c. thickness in mm (where necessary at different depths or distances from the base)
       d. colour
       e. number of zones, depending on 1st order lateral root formation
       f. number of 1st order lateral roots per zone per length unit of the main root
       g. length of the root-hair zone
     2. *1st order lateral roots* (per zone)
       a. shape (elongated, twisted, etc.)

b. length in cm (average + extremes)
c. thickness in mm (average + extremes, where necessary at the base and at various distances from the base)
d. colour
e. number of zones, depending on further lateral root formation
f. number of 2nd order lateral roots, where necessary per zone, in terms of few to very many per unit of length
g. length of the root-hair zone

3. *2nd order lateral roots*
   a. estimated length (average + extremes)
   b. presence of lateral roots of the 3rd and higher orders with estimation of the length
   c. length of the root-hair zone

4. *adventitious roots* (additional roots)
   see under B.I.1, B.I.2, B.I.3

5. *root tubers*
   a. habit (single or combined)
   b. number
   c. place

II. *Monocotyledones* (grasses and cereals)

1. *seminal roots*
   a. shape (elongated, twisted, etc.)
   b. length in cm (average + extremes)
   c. thickness in mm (average + extremes)
   d. colour
   e. number of zones, depending on lateral root formation
   f. number of 1st order lateral roots per unit of length of each zone.

2. *1st order lateral roots*
   a. shape (elongated, twisted, etc.)
   b. length in cm (average + extremes)
   c. thickness in mm (average + extremes)

     d. colour

     e. number of zones, depending on 2nd order lateral root formation

     f. number of 2nd order lateral roots per zone in terms of few to very many per 1st order unit of length.

3. *2nd order lateral roots*

     a. estimated length of 2nd order lateral roots

     b. presence of lateral roots of the 3rd and higher orders and estimates of the length

     c. length of the root-hair zone

4. *nodal roots*

     as B.II.1, B.II.2 and B.II.3

Specific possibilities and difficulties

It may happen that the pinboard is too short for the root system which is to be sampled. In such cases two pinboard specimens can sometimes be taken under each other. The specimens cannot be cut away until the pins of the two pinboards have been driven into the soil. The soil between the two pinboards should be cut through with extreme care.

It is also possible to supplement the data with boring specimens taken from the soil of the hole or its immediate vicinity.

In many cases the pinboard specimen is also used for preserving the profile. In such a case the sample taken is slightly thicker than the length of the pins. This enables the root zone and profile to be compared after they have been washed in the laboratory. This method has been described in a publication (1955) but has since been simplified, the roots being removed from the plastic sheet after drying and transferred to a blackened piece of hardboard to which they are stuck with a colourless glue.

It will be seen from the above that the pinboard method has many possibilities. These specimens can be used to obtain information on all the points listed on pages 10 and 11.

It is also extremely important to obtain an idea of the habit of the root system of a particular plant. Moreover the method is usually fairly easy to carry out and is not very laborious. One drawback is that a fairly large hole has to be made for taking a pinboard specimen and the soil from this hole has to be disposed of in the immediate vicinity. This is not always easy to do on experimental fields. When the specimen is taken from the border of the experimental field the path may be used, but sometimes this is impossible and the crop may be damaged. The soil is usually deposited on a large, sturdy canvas cover; this also prevents the deposited soil from being mixed with the rest and the pit can be filled up more rapidly. Despite this the crop is often damaged over an area of about 4 x 3 sq.m. In most cases this cannot be permitted on small fields in connection with yield determinations, so that in such cases it is generally inadvisable to take more than one sample per plot. Moreover despite the fact that the soil layers are separated during excavation, after the hole has been filled up the profile will never be entirely the same as the original one, and this may be a drawback for experiments continued over a number of years.

2. Examination of soil specimens having a slight volume. The auger method

Material

The auger method is used both in field experiments and certain model experiments. There are two types of augers, one being specially suitable for sampling heavy soils and hardpans. This is the heavy auger which is driven into the soil with a mallet. The other light type is used for sampling light soils, although it is also suitable for heavy soils. Both types were developed by GOEDEWAAGEN (1948) from augers used by VISSER, 1943 (cited by GOEDEWAGEN).

Both augers consist of a cylindrical tube having an inside diameter of 7 cm and a height of 15 cm in the light model and

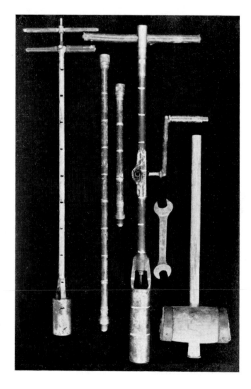

Fig. 11. *Augers used for root sampling, with tools*

25 cm in the heavy one. Until recently use was also made of augers having a 4 cm diameter, but these were less satisfactory on some soils as the frictional resistance of the inner wall is much greater than in the 7 cm auger, and as a result the soil is partly forced away. The cases in which this occurs with the 7 cm auger are so few that they can be ignored, as has been proved by measuring the weights by volume. It may happen, however, that a specimen drilled with the 7 cm auger is not of the same length in both directions; this is usually caused by the compression or expansion of the specimen drilled. Consequently the number of roots found in the specimens when 7 cm augers

are used always corresponds to the original volume of the specimen drilled, even when it has been subject to compression or expansion during drilling. A shaft is fixed to the tube. Marks are made on both the tube and the shaft at 10 cm intervals. A handle is fixed to the top of the shaft to enable the auger to be driven in the soil and pulled out of the hole (Fig. 11).

The shaft of the light auger is 70 or 110 cm in length so that it can be used for drilling to a depth of 80 or 120 cm. The short

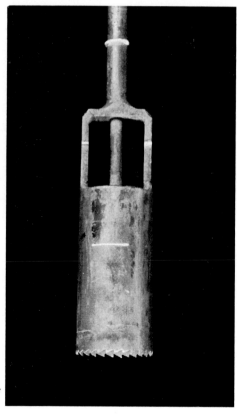

Fig. 12. *The cutting edge of the auger with teeth*

auger is used for the uppermost specimens as in this case the weight of the body is put to better use. The long auger is used for the deeper specimens.

The shaft of both augers consists of a tube containing a rod. A round disc is fastened to the bottom of the rod and can be moved up and down in the tube. A handle is provided at the top of the rod. The rod and stamp are used for forcing the soil specimens out of the tube.

Sampling

The bottom of the tube is serrated (Fig. 12). By slowly twisting the auger to and fro in short turns it is pressed vertically into the soil up to the first mark (Fig. 13). During drilling the stamp is forced upward by the sample. When the auger has reached the required depth it is rotated a number of times so as to free the sample; the auger is then pulled out. The hole is slightly widened by slewing the auger round. This prevents soil and roots from being shaved off by the wall when the next layer is sampled. The sample is then forced out of the tube and collected in a cardboard container where it can be inspected. It is then placed in a numbered paper or plastic bag. The auger is then replaced in the borehole and drilling is continued up to the next mark. The work proceeds until no further roots are encountered in the sample, but to be on the safe side one more sample is taken. If the profile is suitable a drilling sample may be further subdivided into two parts at the interface between two layers. This is usually done with the 0-10 cm layer which is divided in this way into layers of 0-5 and 5-10 cm.

The heavy auger should be of a much heavier design, since it is hammered into the soil. Consequently the auger is provided with a striking head in which can be inserted a sturdy crosspiece which can be used as a handle when the auger is lifted out of the soil. To prevent damage to the material the auger should be hammered fairly gently. Since in heavy soils it is often impossible

Fig. 13. *Drilling a soil sample with a heavy auger*

Fig. 14. *Removing the sample from the auger by turning a handle*

to push the sample out of the auger this is done in another manner. A short rod is fixed to the disc by means of a rack. A housing is mounted on the shaft of the auger about 40 cm above the drilling tube; a cog-wheel can be rotated in this housing with the aid of a pendulum (Fig. 14). The teeth of this cog-wheel engage in the rack. This enables the stamp to be moved up and down and the sample to be pushed out of the auger, after which the same procedure can be followed as that described in the case of the light auger.

The auger may be lengthened by unscrewing the striking head and inserting an extension piece. In clay soils the work, with either the light or the heavy auger, may be greatly facilitated by briefly dipping the auger into a pail of water before each drilling operation.

Calculation of the root weights

The weights of the roots in the drilling samples can only be determined after the specimens have been washed in the laboratory. In some cases, however, they have to be given a pre-treatment. It makes a difference whether or not the samples can be processed immediately, whether the moisture content is determined, or whether the samples consist of sand or clay. Sand samples which are immediately processed on arrival and on which no moisture calculation is carried out, can be washed at once. If the samples, irrespective of the soil of which they consist, cannot be processed immediately, they are dried at about 100° C and stored in the dry state. This is done to prevent the roots from rotting. When the moisture has to be calculated the samples are packed in the field in heat-resistant plastic bags, first weighed together with these bags, and then dried. Afterwards they are weighed again. Clay samples cannot be washed immediately; they should always be first dried and then dispersed in a sodium pyrophosphate solution.

Special precaution should be taken when washing dried samples. If washing were to be carried out immediately the dry, fine roots would be reduced to powder, thus causing losses. To prevent this, dry samples, provided with a label showing the field data, are first pre-soaked in large bottles of water for some eight hours. The addition of 5 cc of detergent in 300 cc of water assists soaking. During this period the roots again take up moisture and become so flexible as to enable them to be washed. For clay samples use is made of an aqueous sodium pyrophosphate solution. This peptises the clay particles, as a result of which the sample often disintegrates altogether. The concentration of the solution is 270 grams of sodium pyrophosphate to 100 l of water.

It is noticeable that although the roots are fairly shrivelled after the samples have been dried, they swell again when the samples are again contacted with water. The roots then substantially regain their normal habit, and even the root hairs

Fig. 15. *Washing a soil sample on a screen*

do not appear to be greatly affected. This means that samples which have first been weighed in a moist condition and then dried and again weighed in order to determine the weight by volume, the pore volume and the soil-water-air ratio, can easily be wetted again and washed for a qualitative and quantitative evaluation of the root fragments in the sample. It would be obvious that this method can be profitably used for studying problems relating to the influence of chemical physical soil properties on root development.

The sample is washed by pouring it out on an approximately 0.3 mm mesh screen of copper gauze. These meshes are so fine that root losses are practically negligible. The screen usually lets through a great deal of the soil, with the exception of clods and coarser soil components (Fig. 15). During washing the roots released are removed from the screen with tweezers and placed in small bottles of water ready to hand (Fig. 16). One drawback

38

Fig. 16. *Washed roots in a formaldehyde solution*

of this washing is that not everyone works with a uniform water jet, so that the operation contains a personal element. Ways are being sought of standardising the procedure.

Once the stage has been reached when no further soil passes through the screen and only very fine roots are left, everything on the screen, viz. rootlets, humus components, plant debris and soil particles, is washed into a glass cylinder in which the soil particles settle, while the roots and the other organic material continue to float for some time. By decanting one or more times and making up the liquid the roots can be separated from the soil, but any plant debris and humus components present will remain in the roots, as they cannot be separated from them by decanting. Finally the mixture is poured on to a fine nylon or muslin screen measuring 10 x 10 cm whence the mass remaining on the screen is added to the other roots that were already separated.

If immediate further processing of the samples is impossible formalin is added. Afterwards the organic impurities should also be removed. This is done by pouring the sample into a shallow enamel dish measuring 26 x 20 x 4 cm. The impurities are removed with tweezers (Fig. 17). When there are many impurities it is of course better to pick the roots out of the mass.

FIG. 17. *Picking out impurities*

One great difficulty is to distinguish living and dead roots, i.e. roots which were alive or dead during sampling. Four features are noted for drawing this distinction, viz. the elasticity of the root, its colour, and the presence of cortex and lateral roots. Dead roots are far less elastic, the colour is often greyer, and the lateral roots have often already broken off, leaving stumps with ravelled ends. The *combined* evaluation of these four features determines whether the root is to be regarded as living or dead. In the latter case it is removed. Another method of distinguishing living roots from dead ones is to contact the roots with a tetra-zolium chloride solution (although this method is not suitable for routine work). Living roots turn red, whereas the dead ones remain colourless (GOEDEWAAGEN, 1954; BUTIJN, 1955 and 1961). After all impurities have been removed from the roots the latter are again poured on to the fine screen and then transferred with tweezers to a paper bag on which all data are noted.

40

The original label is also placed in the bag. Finally the roots are dried in the bags at 75° C. The choice of this unusual temperature was determined by the abnormal conditions immediately after the war. It was found, however, that the results showed little difference from those obtained at a normal temperature of 105° C. A further advantage of this low temperature is that it prevents the roots from being pulverised. The drying takes about 48 hours, after which the bags of roots are placed in an exsiccator to cool down. The roots are then weighed on a torsion balance having an accuracy of 1 mg. Samples of over 500 mg are weighed on a balance having an accuracy of 10 mg.

The object of washing is to remove all *soil particles*, but this is never entirely possible as some particles adhere firmly to the roots, especially when the roots have an abundance of root hairs. Hence the presence of such particles results in an inaccuracy in the root weights obtained. This inaccuracy was determined by us by means of a periodical check in which washed and dried root samples were ashed. It was found that there is usually a relative increase in this impurity the deeper the layers from which the roots were taken. The inaccuracy may increase to a maximum of 12 %. In this connection it is fortunate that the amount of roots found below a depth of about 20 cm is only a small fraction of the total. It can be stated as a general conclusion that when the specimen is carefully washed the impurities need not exceed 4 % at most, based on the entire depth of the hole. In some cases lower values have been found. The organic matter contents of the roots were not determined, although this is also possible with the auger method.

Results

It may be inferred from the above account that the results obtained with the auger method are less extensive than those of the pinboard method. Since one is working with fragments it is impossible to obtain an idea of the root systems as a whole. Nor

TABLE 1. *Reliability of root weights from auger samples of a pasture*

Layers in cms	Total weight of 25 samples	Average weight per sample	σ	m	m %
0-5	3673	147	65	13	8.8
5-10	1112	44	14	3	6.8
10-15	917	37	14	3	8.1
15-20	483	19	9	2	10.5
20-30	544	22	9	2	9.1
30-40	327	13	7	1	7.7
40-50	201	8	5	1	12.5
50-60	158	6	4	1	16.6
60-70	66	3	2	0.4	13.3
70-80	73	3	3	0.6	20.0
80-90	3	sp	0.4	0.09	
Total	*7557*	*302*			

is it possible to make an adequate study of the branching because many lateral roots are wholly or partly cut off by the auger. On the other hand, the auger method provides a good average picture of the root weights of the various soil layers as a large number of samples can be taken without difficulty. As stated above, only a very limited number of samples can be taken with the pinboard method. Moreover, periodic auger samplings can afford an idea of the development of the root system at particular sites. In order to obtain an accurate idea of the roots one should take a large number of samples from which the average values per layer can be calculated. The statistical reliability of these figures can then be determined. An example is given in table 1.

For the purpose of our own investigation the minimum number of borings per plot of such mixed cultures as grassland was put at 25; at least 24 borings are taken of such monocultures as arable crops (where such crops are cultivated in rows, e.g. cereals, 12 borings are taken on the rows and 12 between).

For crops not sown in rows other sites may be selected. The holes are drilled over the field in a selected pattern. Patches overgrown with weed are avoided. Since in most crops the amount by weight of roots in the tilth is 70 % to 90 % of the whole, so that it is very important to calculate this amount with accuracy, it is also possible to adopt the system of making a smaller number of complete borings with an additional number which is confined to the top-soil. Although the accuracy in the root-deficient subsoil is somewhat reduced as a result, there is a slightly greater accuracy in the root-rich tilth. Since each boring is distributed over layers of 10 cm or less, this means that some 250 samples are obtained from 25 complete borings per plot at a drilling depth of 1 metre, all of which samples have to be processed in the laboratory. Consequently this method is very laborious, and this is its great drawback. One advantage is that the field is not damaged to any considerable extent during sampling. Moreover, a very high degree of accuracy can be achieved provided a sufficient number of samples are taken.

Since the auger has a fixed diameter it is possible to calculate the per hectare root production from the root weights per boring. This is important in connection with problems relating to the supply of organic matter to the soil.

Estimate of the root quantities

It was shown above that the calculation of root weights in auger samples is a time-consuming operation. For this reason a method has been developed in which such time-consuming work has been eliminated by making an estimate in the field of the amount of roots in the samples. The aim was to obtain a method which, although slightly less accurate, is adequate for field work and requires little or no laboratory work. This method and the manner in which its final form was reached are fully described in an earlier publication (SCHUURMAN and KNOT, 1957). Here we will only give a brief description of its principle.

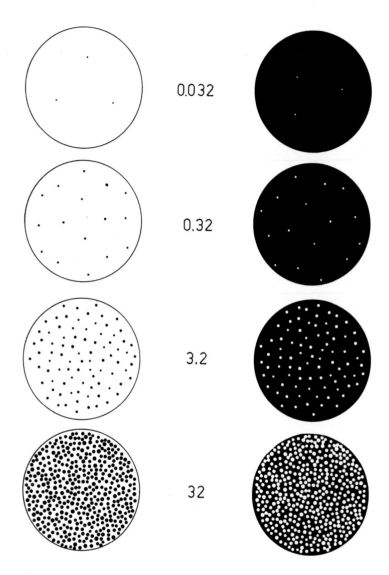

0.032

0.32

3.2

32

Fig. 18. *Some standard figures for use in the evaluation of root quantities*

44

Hitherto the method has only been developed for crops such as grasses and cereals of which the roots have no secondary growth in girth. The method is based on a comparison of root quantities with standard data.

The samples required for the estimate are taken with the auger. After the sample has been removed from the auger it is broken horizontally in the middle, thus breaking the roots which were growing through this plane of fracture. Experience has shown that in most cases this does not occur in the plane of fracture but at a short distance therefrom. This renders them visible and they can be compared with specially designed standard figures. These consist of a number of circles of the same diameter as the auger and in which is made an increasing number of light dots on a dark background in a progressive series (Fig. 18). Each circle has a known dotted area. The total coverage is obtained by summing the coverage percentages of the two planes of fracture. If required the sample can be broken at several points and estimated. This is especially important for samples in which there is a sharp decrease of the amount of roots in a downward direction. It is then possible to calculate the mean coverage of, say, three planes of fractures. In order to eliminate the "dissimilar height" factor of the samples, the coverage figure is multiplied by the height of the sample expressed in centimetres.

Specific possibilities and difficulties

It may easily happen that owing to the great amount of moisture, samples taken with the auger just above the water table are not brought up when the auger is lifted out. This can be prevented by using a light auger of the same design but provided with a leather or rubber aspirator above the stamp (Fig. 19). Since the aspirator runs stiffly it has to be continually lifted a short distance during drilling. When the auger has been pushed in to the required depth the aspirator can be lifted a further

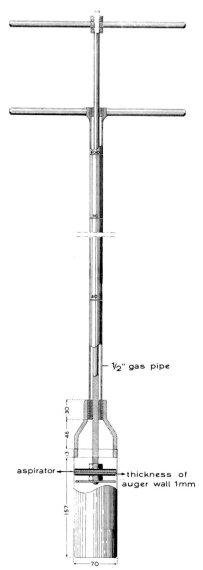

½" gas pipe

aspirator

thickness of
auger wall 1mm

Fig. 19.
Auger provided with an aspirator

46

Fig. 20. *Auger with an extra tube*

short distance in order to dilute the air above the sample in the auger; as a result the sample remains in the auger when it is lifted out.

Good results have also been obtained with an auger round which is fitted an additional drilling tube which is about 2 mm wider than the usual one (Fig. 20). When the auger is lifted the air is able to pass along the outside of the tube, so that no vacuum is formed below the sample.

It may happen that samples have to be taken on very soft soil in which the borehole does not remain entirely open. A similar difficulty occurs when a large number of borings have to be made at a short distance from each other. In such cases use is made of thin-walled iron cylinders having a detachable top-piece secured to the cylinder by means of a bayonet closure. The cylinder together with the top piece has a length of over

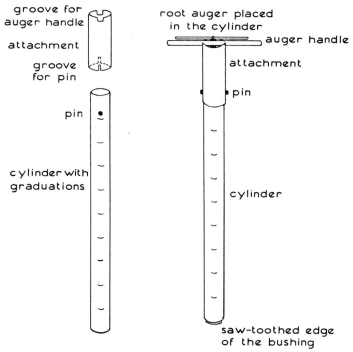

groove for
auger handle

attachment

groove
for pin

pin

cylinder with
graduations

root auger placed
in the cylinder

auger handle

attachment

pin

cylinder

saw-toothed edge
of the bushing

FIG. 21. *Auger and cylinder*

1 metre and a diameter enabling the drilling tube to fit in it with some play. The auger is placed in the cylinder in such a way that the handle of the auger is inserted in the corresponding cavities of the reinforced upper edge of the detachable top-piece (Fig. 21). The saw-teeth of the auger then project some 2 mm below the edge of the cylinder. The cylinder and auger are now pressed into the soil at the same time up to the first mark on the cylinder which is made 9.8 cm from the edge. The auger is then withdrawn, the cylinder remaining in position and descending 10 cm with each subsequent boring until the entire depth has been reached. The detachable top-piece is then

Fig. 22. *Cylinders in the soil.*

removed and can be used for the next boring. The cylinder itself remains in the borehole until all borings have been made, and it can even remain in place afterwards. This may be necessary, for example, in order to support the remainder of the profile when samples have to be taken periodically from a profile of a cylinder experiment. Moreover, the boreholes are sealed off by these cylinders, thus preventing any additional air and moisture from being supplied to the surrounding soil (Fig. 22). This method can also be profitably employed for taking samples in humid soils.

Difficulties may also be encountered when taking auger samples on peat soils. In the first place the peat may be too loose or so stratified that the auger is unable to penetrate it. Nor is it immediately possible to wash out all the peat from a sample without roots being lost. However there are indications that a pre-treatment with a 5 % hydrogen peroxide solution has a good effect. Peat also leads to difficulties in washing when samples are taken with pinboards, although the drawbacks in this case are less considerable as an idea can be formed of the structure of the root system from the pinboard which is still partly covered with peat. Moreover, with careful handling the peat can be removed with tweezers.

When taking auger samples a further difficulty may arise which is equally applicable to the pinboard method. This is the case when the soil is very stony. Both methods are then equally impracticable. Should it nevertheless be necessary to assemble data, in such a case use may be made of the method developed by WEAVER (1926) in which the root development is studied in a profile wall.

To sum up, it may be stated that both the pinboard and auger method have their own particular advantages and disadvantages and that the data not supplied by one method can be supplimented from the other. Consequently it is sometimes advisable to employ both methods at the same time.

3. Investigation of profile walls

Weaver's method

Weaver's method, as referred to above, is used for this purpose.

Mapping, followed by counting

This method was developed by OSKAMP and BATJER (1932) for trees and was afterwards slightly modified and supplemented by ourselves. In this method a trench is dug at a certain distance from a tree and the ends of the cut roots are mapped in one of the walls of the cavity. This can be done by covering the wall with a system of squares of, say, 20 x 20 cm (Fig. 23), nails being driven into the profile wall at 20 cm intervals round the sampling area. Pieces of string weighted on the bottom are suspended on the horizontal row of nails, so that they hang vertically along

FIG. 23. *Squares on a profile wall*

the wall. Pieces of string weighted at either end are also suspended over the corresponding nails of the two vertical rows, thus forming the horizontal lines. The wall is then carefully scraped with a long needle with no too sharp a point (sack needle with a handle) so as to render visible the ends of the cut-off roots. These are mapped, the different categories being distinguished according to thickness. A different symbol is used for each category (Fig. 24). The profile can be sketched in on the map at the same time. It may be asked how the trench should be excavated with respect to the tree. The two chief possibilities are tangential and radial trenches. Some variation has been found in a tangential trench, but it is more or less immaterial on which side of the tree the trench is dug provided identical conditions obtain round the tree, e.g. the structure of the profile and the hydrological regime (tables 2 and 3). A tangential wall can then be divided into a number of parts of equal size which may be taken as replicates. Actually this division has already been made by the system of squares during the sampling process. This is important as it means that the root zones can also be compared at different times by always

TABLE 2. *Comparison of the numbers of roots of apple trees on a grass plot in tangential trenches at equal distances from the tree*

Layer cm	Distance from the tree 200 cm — Width of the profile 120 cm (= 1/12 circumference) — Numbers of roots per trench					Percentages per trench					Distance from the tree 150 cm — Width of the profile 80 cm (= 1/12 circumference) — Numbers of roots per trench			Percentages per trench		
	1	2	3	4	Av.	1	2	3	4	Av.	1	2	Av.	1	2	Av.
DIAMETER OF THE ROOTS <½ mm																
0- 10	0	13	4	0	4	0	10	2	0	3	8	14	11	6	6	6
10- 40	22	29	27	42	30	17	22	15	34	22	33	75	54	25	33	29
40- 70	52	27	75	47	50	39	20	40	38	35	34	82	58	25	36	32
70-100	43	39	52	16	38	32	30	28	13	26	37	51	44	28	23	24
100-150	16	24	25	19	21	10	18	13	15	14	22	5	14	16	2	9
Total	*133*	*132*	*183*	*124*	*143*						*134*	*227*	*181*			
DIAMETER OF THE ROOTS ½-1 mm																
0- 10	1	3	3	0	2	4	13	10	0	7	4	2	3	12	4	8
10- 40	9	12	3	13	9	37	54	10	30	30	8	10	9	24	21	22
40- 70	8	4	15	18	11	33	18	48	42	37	10	15	12	29	31	30
70-100	3	2	3	7	4	12	9	10	16	13	11	18	14	31	37	35
100-150	3	1	7	5	4	12	5	22	12	13	1	3	2	3	6	5
Total	*24*	*22*	*31*	*43*	*30*						*34*	*48*	*40*			

TABLE 3. *Comparison of the numbers of roots of apple trees on a straw mulch plot in tangential trenches at equal distances from the tree*

| | Distance from the tree 200 cm — Width of the profile 120 cm (= 1/12 circumference) | | | | | | | | | | Distance from the tree 150 cm — Width of the profile 80 cm (1/12 circumference) | | | | | |
| | Numbers of roots per trench | | | | | Percentages per trench | | | | | Numbers of roots per trench | | | Percentages per trench | | |
Layer cm	1	2	3	4	Av.	1	2	3	4	Av.	1	2	Av.	1	2	Av.
	DIAMETER OF THE ROOTS $< \frac{1}{2}$ mm															
0- 10	130	161	97	98	122	36	45	30	32	36	104	78	91	36	28	32
10- 40	135	80	118	120	113	37	22	37	39	34	87	98	92	30	35	33
40- 70	21	31	54	40	37	6	9	17	13	11	29	41	35	10	15	12
70-100	27	28	24	25	26	8	8	8	8	8	31	29	30	11	10	11
100-150	49	56	25	23	38	13	16	8	8	11	37	31	34	13	11	12
Total	362	356	318	306	336						288	277	282			
	DIAMETER OF THE ROOTS $\frac{1}{2}$-1 mm															
0- 10	10	29	16	16	18	16	32	26	20	24	17	8	12	22	16	19
10- 40	36	28	32	35	33	58	31	52	43	44	36	24	30	46	47	47
40- 70	7	19	10	15	13	11	21	16	19	17	13	6	10	17	12	15
70-100	8	10	4	9	8	13	11	6	11	11	10	7	8	13	14	13
100-150	1	4	0	6	3	2	4	0	7	4	2	6	4	2	12	6
Total	62	90	62	81	75						78	51	64			

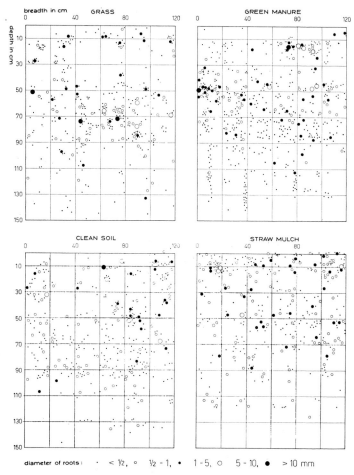

FIG. 24. *Example of mapping roots in a profile wall*

taking samples from different points on the circle. The radial trench affords an idea of the root development at different distances from a tree. Since in such a map each root has its own

TABLE 4. *Comparison of the numbers of roots at three different distances from the tree*

Diameter of the roots in mm	Width of the trench 1/12 circumference Distance from the tree		
	2 metres	1.50 metres	1.00 metre
	STRAW MULCH PLOT		
$<\frac{1}{2}$	336	282	272
$\frac{1}{2}$-1	75	64	54
1-5	32	36	28
5-10	7	6	6
>10	2	5	4
	GRASS COVERED PLOT		
$<\frac{1}{2}$	143	181	150
$\frac{1}{2}$-1	30	40	36
1-5	14	22	16
5-10	4	2	3
>10	1	1	0

distance from the tree there can be no question of replicates, and this means that the data provided by a radial trench are less reliable. The reliability can, however, be enhanced by sampling a greater number of radial walls per tree, or both walls of a radial trench.

Tangential trenches can also afford an impression of the root development at different distances from a tree when they are dug at varying distances from the trunk (table 4).

It may be asked what agreement exists in the results obtained from two trees subjected to the same treatment. This is found by sampling two trees of four experimental plots in the same way in tangential trenches. Fig. 25 shows this data for the various categories of roots in the various soil layers. It can be seen that in many cases there is reasonably good agreement between the amounts of roots found.

For processing the data mapped the number of roots is summed per square per category. From this it is possible to calculate the total number of roots in each layer. If necessary

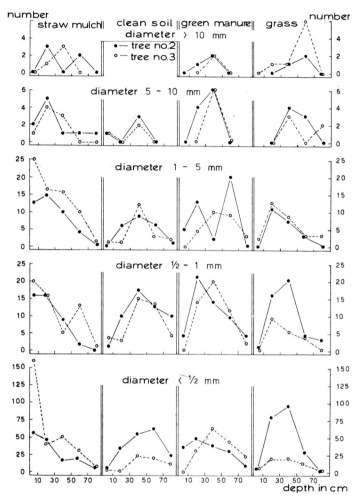

Fig. 25. *Comparison of the root systems of two trees subjected to the same treatment*

the average number of roots can be determined per unit of length of a layer and the statistical reliability calculated.

56

The mapping method discussed above can provide important information on the root development of woody plants. It has, however, a number of limitations, as in the first place it is very time-consuming, so that it is practically impossible to sample more than one tree in a plot, and secondly, as all work has to be done outdoors, good weather is essential. The latter is actually the predominant factor, unless, of course, a tent and artificial light are used. In conclusion, it should be pointed out that the sampling depth is governed by the water table.

A variant of this method can be used in sandy soil. In this case the soil can be flushed out with water instead of being worked loose with a needle. A knapsack sprayer or vaporizer can be used for this purpose. When a wall is sprayed with the finest atomizer the cut-off roots show up well and can be mapped. Only a small amount of water is required. This method is also used by other research workers.

III. Container experiments

In these experiments plants are grown under specific, pre-determined conditions. In some experiments several of the above-mentioned methods may be used, but the procedure in many container experiments is often so adapted to root studies that the processing has its own particular character. The following will be discussed in succession: experiments with *cylinders*, *cases*, *boxes and pots* filled with soil, and cylinders filled with nutrient solutions (water cultures).

1. Cylinder experiments

Material

Cylinders of different dimensions are used. Concrete cylinders were first used by GOEDEWAAGEN (FRANKENA and GOEDEWAAGEN, 1942). The original, laborious method has since been improved and simplified and new facilities created. Use is made of *concrete* cylinders having an inside diameter of 30 cm and a height of 100 or 125 cm, and *eternit* cylinders having an inside diameter of 15 and 30 cm and a height of 75 cm. The concrete cylinders are arranged in groups of 18 in large, hollowed-out concrete vessels. The cylinders are filled with soil. A cylinder filled with soil has a total weight of about 200 kg. The upper edge of the cylinders is about level with the surrounding surface (Fig. 26). A given soil water level can be maintained in the concrete vessels. The water table required does not necessarily have to be constant, – a varying level may also be used. The eternit cylinders are usually in vans, so that the experiment can be conducted either out-of-doors or under cover, depending on the weather (Fig. 27).

FIG. 26.   *View of a part of an experiment with concrete cylinders*

FIG. 27.   *View of an experiment with eternit cylinders on a van*

59

Filling of the concrete cylinders

The soil with which the cylinders are to be filled is first screened. The screened soil is mixed with fertilizers as well as possible and stored in plastic bags to prevent loss of moisture. The moisture content is determined so as to enable a calculation to be made of the amount of soil to be introduced into the cylinder in order to obtain a predetermined density. This amount of soil is weighed and divided up into portions of a few kg which are again stored in plastic bags. Each portion is large enough to enable the cylinder to be filled with a 5 cm layer. During each filling operation half a bag is emptied into the cylinder and then tamped down. A regular check is made to ensure that the proper level is reached after tamping. If this is the case the soil along the edge of the tube is pressed down lightly with an curved iron bar (Fig. 28) so as to prevent growth conditions for the roots being more favourable in this part than in the rest of the profile. The topmost layer of from 2 to 5 mm

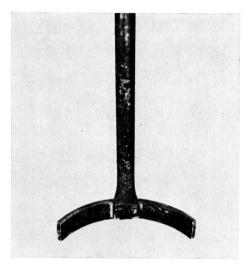

Fig. 28.
Apparatus for compressing the soil along the wall of the cylinder

is then again carefully scraped loose over the entire surface to prevent the formation of layers (GOEDEWAAGEN, 1932, p. 182). The second half of the soil is then poured into the cylinder and treated in the same way. Half a bag of soil is then again poured into the cylinder, and so on until the cylinder is entirely full. In this manner it is possible to build up a great diversity of profiles with variations in soil type and density. A particular crop may be grown on these profiles. Since the soil is capable of absorbing a great deal of moisture in the initial stages, the vessels are regularly replenished until an equilibrium has been reached. The crop can then be sown.

Soil water level

The level of the water in the vessel used in the concrete cylinder experiment is checked several times a week (and hence the water table also). If rainfall has made it too high the excess water is pumped out and measured. If the soil water level has fallen it is made up. These amounts are also measured, as well as the amounts of precipitation. This affords an idea of the amounts of water which the plants are capable of absorbing. It is advisable to cover the top of the profile with a layer of fine gravel of two or more cm to prevent moisture evaporating from the soil.

Sampling

There are various ways of studying the root development of a crop. It has already been shown on page 49 how a profile can be drilled in a concrete cylinder (Fig. 22). Experience has shown that these cylinders can be used for taking at least 6 borings from a tube having a diameter of 30 cm.

A second possibility is to remove all soil from the cylinder layer by layer. This can be done by first removing some samples

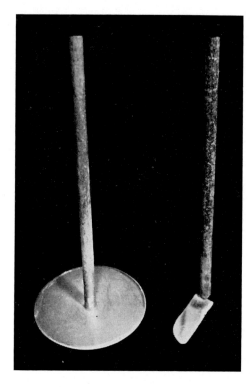

Fig. 29.
*Knives used for cutting
away soil horizontally in
cylinder experiments*

with an auger up to the required depth and then cutting loose
the rest of the soil to the same depth by means of a specially
designed knives (Fig. 29) and taking it out of the tube. The
drilling samples may be kept separate, e.g. for moisture deter-
mination, and added to the remainder. The resultant samples
may be washed in the manner discussed under II - 2.

A third possibility is to lift the tube out of the vessel with the
profile and crop and to lay it on a frame. To prevent the profile
from falling out of the tube as it is removed, the tube and profile
are placed on a steel plate and hoisted while standing on this
plate. On the frame the top of the profile should be lower than the

Fig. 30. *Removing impurities from a root system after washing*

bottom. The tube should not have a gradient of more than 30°
as otherwise there is a risk of the profile slipping out of the tube.
The soil can then be washed out of the tube. In most cases it is
best to do this when the soil has been washed from the bottom of
the tube. The presence of a large number of roots in the top
layer makes it difficult to wash the soil from the top. When the
profile has been washed away from the bottom one can immediately note the depth to which the roots have penetrated into
the soil. As washing proceeds the gradient can be reduced. In
the last stage of washing the tube can be so placed that the top
of the profile is highest. When the entire root system has been
washed free of soil it is carefully slid out of the tube on to a glass
plate with the use of large amounts of water. Any extraneous
matter is removed in a shallow enamel dish of water (Fig. 30).
The root system can then be photographed. In conclusion, the
root system and the individual roots can be described in the
manner indicated on pages 28, ff.

One drawback of the third method is that no data is obtained
on the moisture content of the soil. This disadvantage may be
overcome by drilling samples out of the profile with a narrow
drill (diameter 14 mm) before the soil is washed away (Fig. 31),

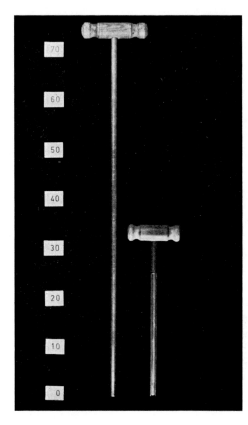

Fig. 31.
*Drills used for taking
small samples for moisture
determinations*

but owing to the fineness of the drill it is not possible to make a hole deeper than about 60 cm. This drilling results in slight damage to the root system.

Filling of the eternit cylinders

The eternit cylinders are usually above ground. They are filled with soil in exactly the same manner as the concrete cylinders. It is advisable to give the bottom of the profiles a

Fig. 32.
*Eternit cylinders in dishes
of water covered with
plastic collars*

permanent support, which is done by securing moisture-per-
meable nylon cloth to the bottom of the cylinders. In general
the same kind of experiments can be carried out with these
cylinders as with the concrete ones. Since they are lighter they
are easier to handle, but the cylinders with a diameter of 15 cm
do not take as many plants.

Soil water level

The soil water levels may be varied by placing the cylinders
in dishes of different heights. To prevent the water from evaporating from these dishes they are covered with a collar of plas-

tic material (Fig. 32). Evaporation from the profile is prevented by covering it with a layer of fine gravel, in the same way as the above-mentioned concrete cylinders. The water used for replenishing the vessels is measured, so that the moisture uptake of the plant in each cylinder can be accurately determined.

Sampling

The root zone investigation is simply done by washing away the soil, as discussed in connection with the concrete cylinders. Where there is a large amount of roots it is possible in these experiments to divide the cylinders in half in the lengthwise direction. Although the cylinder is destroyed as a result the washing process is facilitated. In this connection we are looking for a possible use for cylinders sawn through in the longitudinal direction. Moisture samples are taken with the small drill (Fig. 31).

Hitherto we have only discussed cylindrical tubes, but it is obvious that both the shape and material may be adapted to circumstances.

Cylinder experiments can be undertaken with natural profiles as well as artificial ones. In an investigation carried out by FRANKENA and GOEDEWAAGEN (1942) a steel tube with a cutting edge was driven into the soil. This tube had a diameter of 30 cm, which was equal to the inside diameter of the concrete cylinders. After being excavated the profile was transferred to a concrete cylinder.

However, later experiments showed that it was possible, and probably even better, to excavate a soil column having a diameter of 30 cm on which the cylinder stands. As the soil is dug more deeply and cut away, the cylinder gradually falls round this soil column by its own weight. Use may be made of a metal collar with a 30 cm diameter and provided with a cutting edge. In this case the cylinder rests on the metal collar which it forces downward. This method can only be used in soils with a firm profile structure, i.e. the soil should not be too wet and not too dry. Should it be too dry, one can attempt to make things easier by wetting the soil. Hitherto better results have been obtained with glazed earthenware cylinders than with the fairly rough concrete cylinders.

Undisturbed soil samples have been obtained in a similar manner in tins having a diameter of 25 cm and a height of 20 cm.

FIG. 33.   *Wooden cases used for root studies*

FIG. 34. *Replacing one wall of a wooden case by a pinboard*

2. Experiments in cases and boxes

Cases of various designs are used for root examinations. In the first place wooden cases were used by GOEDEWAAGEN (1932, 1933), following ROTMISTROFF (1908) and MASCHHAUPT (1915). The dimensions are length 60 cm, width 20 cm and depth 100 cm (Fig. 33). The cases are filled with soil and then buried. A crop can be grown on the 60 x 20 cm top surface. When the time has come to examine the crop, one wall measuring 100 x 60 cm and fastened with screws is unscrewed and replaced by a pinboard of the same dimensions of which the pins are driven into the profile (Fig. 34). The whole is then laid flat with the pinboard underneath and the case removed. The result is a pinboard sample which can be washed by the method described above and further processed.

There are two types of concrete boxes which are also in use. One type is a ready-made box of which the walls are fastened together. Its dimensions are 50 x 50 x 50 cm. The only way of

FIG. 35. *Small wooden case with one glass panel provided with squares*

studying root development in such boxes is by means of borings, as it is hardly possible to obtain pinboard samples.

The second type of box is made of loose rectangular concrete plates fitted together so as to form boxes measuring 1 x 1 x 1 metre. It is therefore advisable to bury the plates; during sampling a hole can be dug on the side of the box, after which the adjoining side-plate can be removed. After the soil has been partly sliced off to prevent marginal effects, a pinboard sample can be taken.

A particular method of root investigation is that in which root growth is observed behind glass.

GOEDEWAAGEN (1955) carried out experiments in small wooden boxes of which one vertical wall was replaced by a glass panel. The inside area of these boxes is 10 x 10 cm and the height 25 cm. A network of squares may be arranged on the glass panel to facilitate observation. The boxes are slightly tilted so that the glass wall leans forward. The glass wall should be covered during the experiment and the cover only removed when observations are made. The boxes are suitable for short experiments in which the root growth can be observed through the glass (Fig. 35). At the end of the experiment the roots may be washed free by removing the glass panel and replacing it with a pinboard.

3. Pot cultures

In this case also different variations are possible. Use is made of ordinary flower pots, Mitscherlich pots, and combinations of pots and water cultures. The glazed earthenware vessels may also be mentioned under this heading, as owing to their size they belong here rather than to the boxes. Such pots can be filled in the same way as the cylinders. In the case of flower pots it should be remembered that the diameter is not the same at all points.

Pot culture experiments are particularly useful when it is

required to examine the plants at an early stage of growth and no fully-grown root systems are required.

The drawbacks of pots are usually the shallow depth and slight volume, as a result of which the root depth is also limited. Consequently the root systems of plants grown in pots are often very divergent from those grown under natural conditions. This is further exaggerated by the extremely intense root growth along the walls, as is often seen in porous flower pots. Owing to this, pot culture experiments are of limited use for root studies. This drawback is less applicable to the above-mentioned glazed earthenware vessels which are 25 cm long, 25 cm wide and 50 cm deep.

Root investigation of plants grown in pots can only be properly carried out provided the entire root system is washed free. This can be done by washing away the soil in a downward direction, although it is sometimes also possible to remove the entire contents from the pot and then wash them.

MASCHHAUPT (1911) used a combination of flower pot and glass cylinder, widening as far as possible the opening in the bottom of ordinary flower pots so as to give roots a better chance of growing out of the pot. This opening was covered with a thin film of cottonwool to prevent soil from falling into the beaker of nutrient solution underneath the pot. In the middle of the pot was arranged a wooden stick having a slight downward taper and a diameter about equal to that of the opening in the bottom. The soil was pressed in round the stick. After the stick had been removed the hole was filled up fairly loosely with earth. A cavity was made in the middle in which was placed a germinated seed.

The pots were placed in round holes made in cases with detachable side walls, so that the beakers of nutrient solution were in the dark. The root growth could be observed at regular intervals by removing one of the side walls.

GOEDEWAAGEN (1955) employed a method which is substantially the same as MASCHHAUPT's. Eternit pots were used of which the bottom consisted of wire netting with a 2 mm mesh.

Fig. 36. *View of a pot-cylinder experiment*

This wire netting was covered with a thin layer of glass wool. The pots were filled with soil and placed on glass cylinders filled with water or nutrient solution. In this way the subsoil was imitated. Glass wool prevents soil particles from falling through the gauze but permits free passage of the roots. The soil and water were separated by a thin layer of air.

At the transition from pot to cylinder a metal collar was used to prevent aeration and evaporation of the water in the cylinder, and in order to create a moist medium in the layer of air between the soil and the water. A double layer of white plastic material was wrapped round the eternit pots to prevent evaporation through the wall of the cylinder (Fig. 36). An experimental plan of this kind is very suitable for studying the importance of subsoil roots for the plant's supply of moisture. It is also possible to study fertilization problems in the topsoil and subsoil.

The soil in the pots was covered with a layer of gravel. The amount of water consumed by the plants was calculated by weighing the pots and cylinders separately at regular intervals.

The roots in the glass cylinders may be studied without making any further provisions, and it is even possible to measure the longitudinal growth of the roots during the experiment. The topsoil roots should be washed free.

4. Water cultures

ZIJLSTRA (1922) germinated seeds on an annular glass tube having a diameter of 13 cm on which was stretched gauze. The ring floated in a jar of water so that the gauze just touched the surface and the seeds placed on it came into contact with the water. After germination the roots grew through the meshes of the gauze and were freely suspended in the water. The main root was immediately marked. Afterwards cultures were grown in nutrient solutions in $2\frac{1}{2}$ litre glass cylinders 24 cm in height.

Water cultures are comparatively rarely used for root studies, conditions differing so extensively from field conditions that it is often very difficult to compare the conclusions. In general they may be used for fertilisation and aeration problems. Cylinders or glass vessels of different sizes may be used for the purpose. The growth of algae in the water or nutrient solution may cause undesirable changes. This can be prevented by covering the vessel with black paper, black plastic material or corrugated paper. But it should still be borne in mind that it may be necessary to replenish and aerate the water regularly. The root system can be easily studied by temporarily removing the cover.

Bibliography

1 ALBRECHT, D., 1951. ,,Verbesserung der Spatendiagnose." Die Deutsche Landwirtschaft 2: 41-43

2 ALBRECHT, D., 1955. ,,Verbessertes Verfahren der Freilegung der Wurzelkrone unter Beibehaltung ihrer natürlichen Lage." Arch. f. Gartenbau 3: 11-16

3 ALBRECHT, D., K. H. FRITZSCHE und C. WINKLER, 1953. ,,Weitere Entwicklung des Strukturbohres." Die Deutsche Landwirtschaft 4: 206-208

4 AMSON, F. W. van, 1954 ,,Wortelonderzoek op enkele grasproefvelden van het Lelydorpplan." De Surinaamse Landbouw 2: 229-235

5 ATHERTON LEE, H., 1926. ,,The distribution of the roots of young D 1135 plant cane in the soil." Hawaiian Planters Record XXX: 267, 511, 520, 523

6 BÄR, K. und O. TSERETHELI, 1943. ,,Der Einfluss der Schnitthäufigkeit auf die Wurzelentwicklung junger Luzerne." Pflanzenbau 19: 317-328

7 BAUMANN, H. und M. L. KLAUS, 1955. ,,Über die Wurzelbildung bei hohem Grundwasserstand." Z.f. Acker-u. Pfl. bau 99: 410-426

8 BAVEL, C. H. M. van, 1953. ,,Het bestuderen van wortelsystemen met radio-actieve isotopen." Landbk. T. 65: 33-34

9 BERKMANN, M., 1913.,,Untersuchungen über den Einfluss der Pflanzenwurzeln auf die Struktur des Bodens." Int. Mitt. f. Bodenk. 3: 1-49

10 BLAAUW, A. H., 1938. ,,De betekenis van de grondwaterstand voor de bloembollencultuur." Verh. Kon. Acad. Wet. A'dam Afd. Natuurk. 2e Sectie, D 37, No 1

11 BLOODWORTH, M. E., C. A. BURLESON and W. R. COWLEY, 1958. ,,Root distribution of some irrigated crops using undisrupted soil cores." Agron.J. 50: 317-320

12 BÖHME, H., 1925. ,,Untersuchungen über die Bewurzelung der Industriekartoffeln." J. Landwirt. 73: 81-144

13 BOHNE, H., 1949. ,,Bemerkungen zu den Arbeiten von S. Gericke (Die Bedeutung der Ernterückstände für den Humushaushalt des Bodens). Z. f. Pfl. ern. D. u. Bodk. 44: 65-71

14 BOHNE, H. und J. GARVERT, 1951. ,,Untersuchungen über die Bedeutung der Ernterückstände des Getreides für die Humusversorgung." Z. f. Pfl. ern. D. u. Bodk. 55: 170-178

15 BOONSTRA, A. E. H. R., 1931. ,,Root systems of seven varieties of peas grown under similar cultural conditions." Meded. Landbouwhogeschool 35, Verh. 2, 62 pp.
16 BOSCH, D. v. d., 1952. ,,Wortelonderzoek met eenvoudige hulpmiddelen." Maandbl. v. d. Landb. voorl. d. 9: 335-341
17 BRENCHLEY, W. E. and V. G. JACKSON, 1921. ,,Root development in barley and wheat under different conditions of growth." Ann. Bot. 35: 533-556.
18 BROUWER, R., 1959. ,,De invloed van de worteltemperatuur op de groei van erwten." Jaarb. Inst. Biol. en Scheik. Ond. v. Landb. gew. Meded. 73: 27-36
19 BROWN, E. M., 1943. ,,Seasonal variations in the growth and chemical composition of Kentucky Bluegrass." Missouri Agric. Expl. Stat. Res. Bull. 360, 56 pp.
20 BUTIJN, J., 1955. ,,Bewortelingsproblemen in de fruitteelt." De plantenwortel in de landbouw: 156-168
21 BUTIJN, J., 1961. ,,Bodembehandeling in de fruitteelt." Versl. Landbouwk. Onderz. 66.7, 403 pp.
22 CLEVERINGA, C. J., 1955. ,,Het onderzoek van plantenwortels in hun natuurlijke groeimilieu met behulp van eenvoudige middelen." De plantenwortel in de landbouw: 192-198
23 COSTER, C., 1932. ,,Wortelstudiën in de tropen." Med. Bosb. Proefst. No. 31, 96 pp.
24 CRIST, J. W. and J. E. WEAVER, 1924. ,,Absorption of nutrients from subsoil in relation to crop yield." Bot. Gaz. 77: 121-148
25 DAVIS, B. M., 1924. ,,Root development of lucerne." N. Z. J. Agric. 28: 179-180
26 DEAN, A. L., 1929. ,,Root observation boxes." Phytopath. 19: 407-412
27 DEHÉRAIN, P. 1902. ,,Traité de chimie agricole." Paris
28 DETMER, W., 1872. ,,Über den Einfluss äusserer Verhältnisse auf die Wurzelentwicklung." Die Landwirtsch. Versuchsstat. 15: 107
29 EATON, F. M., 1941. ,,Water uptake and root growth as influenced by inequalities in the concentration of the substrate." Plant Physiol. 16: 545-564
30 FARRIS, N. F., 1934. ,,Root habits of certain crop plants as observed in the humid soils of New Yersey." Soil Sci. 38: 87-111
31 FEHRENBACHER, J. B. and J. D. ALEXANDER, 1955. ,,A method for studying corn root distribution using a soil-core sampling machine and shaker-type washer." Agron. J. 47: 468-472
32 FERRANT, N. A. J. and H. B. SPRAGUE, 1940. ,,Effect of treating different horizons of sassafras loam on root development of red clover." Soil Sci. 50: 141-161

33 Fox, R. L. and R. C. Lipps, 1955. ,,Influence of soil-profile characteristics upon the distribution of roots and nodules of alfalfa and sweet clover." Agron. J. *47:* 361-367

34 Frank, B., 1893. ,,Die Assimilation des freien Stickstoffs durch die Pflanzenwelt." Bot. Ztg. *51:* 139-156

35 Frankena, H. J. en M. A. J. Goedewaagen, 1942. ,,Een vakkenproef over de invloed van verschillende waterstanden op de grasgroei bij drie grondsoorten." Versl. Landbouwk. Onderz. *48A:* 407-462

36 Freckmann, W., 1926. ,,Bericht über die Tätigkeit des Instituts für Meliorationswesen und Moorkultur." Landwirtsch. Jahrb. *64,* Ergänzungsband I-II: 34-62

37 Frese, H., W. Czeratzky und H. J. Altemüller, 1955. ,,Über die Wirkung der Verteilung organischer und anorganischer Düngerstoffe im Boden auf das Wurzelwachstum von Zuckerrüben." Z. f. Pfl. ern. D. u. Bodk. *69:* 198-205

38 Fribourg, H. A., 1953. ,,A rapid method for washing roots." Agron. J. *45:* 334-335

39 Früwirth, C., 1895. ,,Über die Ausbildung des Wurzelsystems der Hülsenfrüchte." Wollney: Agrikulturphysik *18:* 461-479

40 Gates, C. T., 1951. ,,The quantitative recovery of root systems in pot experiments." The J. of the Australian Inst. of Agric. Sci. *17:* 152-153

41 Gericke, S., 1945. ,,Die Bedeutung der Ernterückstände für den Humushaushalt des Bodens. 1e Teil. Die Ergebnisse bisheriger Untersuchungen." Z. f. Pfl. ern , D. u. Bodk. *35:* 229-247

42 Gericke, S., 1946. ,,Idem, 2e Teil." Z. f. Pfl. ern. D. u. Bodk. *37:* 46-61

43 Gile, P. L. and J. O. Carrero, 1917. ,,Absorption of nutrients as affected by the number of roots supplied with the nutrient." J. Agric. Res. *9:* 73-95

44 Gist, G. R. and R. M. Smith, 1948. ,,Root development of several common forage grasses to a depth of eighteen inches." J. Amer. Soc. Agron. *40:* 1036-1042

45 Gliemeroth, G., 1952. ,,Wasserhaushalt des Bodens in Abhängigkeit von der Wurzelausbildung einiger Kulturpflanzen." Z. f. Acker-u. Pfl. bau *95:* 21-46

46 Gliemeroth, G., 1953. ,,Bearbeitung und Düngung des Unterbodens in ihrer Wirkung auf Wurzelentwicklung, Stoffaufnahme und Pflanzenleistung." Z. f. Acker-u. Pfl. bau *96:* 1-44

47 Goedewaagen, M. A. J., 1932. ,,De groei van het wortelstelsel der planten bij gelijke en bij ongelijke vruchtbaarheid van boven- en ondergrond." Versl. Landbouw. Onderz. *38A:* 179-199

48 Goedewaagen, M. A. J., 1933. ,,Het wortelstelsel der graanplanten bij gelijke en ongelijke verdeling der meststoffen in de grond." Versl. Landbouwk. Onderz. *39A:* 243-266

77

49 GOEDEWAAGEN, M. A. J., 1942. ,,Het wortelstelsel der landbouwgewassen." 173 pp.

50 GOEDEWAAGEN, M. A. J., 1948. ,,De methoden, die aan het Landbouwproefstation en Bodemkundig Instituut T.N.O. te Groningen bij het wortelonderzoek op bouw- en grasland in gebruik zijn." 11 pp. Groningen, Inst. Bodemvruchtbaarheid.

51 GOEDEWAAGEN, M. A. J., 1949. ,,Een en ander over de methodiek van het wortelonderzoek op bouw- en grasland." Maandblad v. d. R.L.V.D. 6,5: 194-200

52 GOEDEWAAGEN, M. A. J., 1954. ,,Beoordeling van de vitaliteit van het wortelstelsel." Landbk. T. 66: 553-554

53 GOEDEWAAGEN, M. A. J., 1955. ,,De oecologie van het wortelstelsel der gewassen." De plantenwortel in de landbouw: 31-69

54 GÖRBING, J., 1947. ,,Die Spatendiagnose." Schriftenreihe: Neuaufbau von Boden her, Heft 7

55 GÖRBING, J., 1948. ,,Die Grundlage der Gare im praktischen Ackerbau." Band I u. II

56 GORDIENKO, M., 1930. ,,Über die Beziehungen zwischen Bodenbeschaffenheit und Wurzelgestaltung bei jungen Pflanzen." Landwirtsch. Jahrb. 72: 125-139

57 HAAS, H. J. and G. A. ROGLER, 1953. ,,A technique of photographing grass roots in situ." Agron. J. 45: 173

58 HANSON, W. R. and L. A. STODDART, 1940. ,,Effects of grazing upon bunch wheat grass." J. Amer. Soc. Agron. 32: 278-289

59 HAYS, W. M., 1889. ,,Corn, its habit of root growth, methods of planting and cultivating notes on ears and stools or suckers." Minn. Agric. Exp. Stat. Bull. 35: 47-58

60 HELLRIEGEL, H., 1883. ,,Wurzel und Bodenvolumen." Beitr. Naturw. Grundl. Ackerbaus: 119-280

61 HENDRICKSON, A. H. and F. J. VEIHMEYER, 1931. ,,Influence of dry soil on root extension." Plant Phys. 6: 567-576

62 HESSE, H., 1903. ,,Beitrage zur Morphologie und Biologie der Wurzelhaare." Inaug. Diss. Jena.

63 HESSELINK, E., 1926. ,,Een en ander over de wortelontwikkeling van de grove den en de Oostenrijkse den." Meded. Rijksbosbouwproefstat. Deel II, afl. 3

64 HOPKINS, H., 1953. ,,Root development of grasses on revegetated land." J. Range Mgmt 6: 382-392

65 HOSÄUS, A., 1870-72. ,,Ob und in wieweit die physikalischen Eigenschaften eines Bodens von Einfluss sind auf die Bewurzelung von Gerste und Rüben." Jahrb. Agric. Chemie, S 64

66 HÖVELER, W., 1892. ,,Über die Verwertung des Humus bei der Ernährung der chlorophyllführenden Pflanzen." Jahrb. Wiss. Bot. 24: 283

67 HUDIG, J., 1939. „Klinisch grondonderzoek in de tropen." Landbk. T. *51:* 372-389

68 JACQUES, W. A., 1937. „A new type of root sampler." N.Z.J. Sci. Technol. *19:* 267-270

69 JACQUES, W. A., 1937. „The effect of different rates of defoliation on the root development of certain grasses." N.Z.J. Sci. Technol. *19:* 441-450

70 JONKER, J. J., 1958. „Bewortelingsonderzoek en ondergrondbewerking in de Noordoostpolder." Diss. Wageningen, 164 pp.

71 KAMPE, K., 1929. „Studien über Bewurzelungsstärke und Wurzeleindringungsvermögen verschiedener Kulturpflanzen." Arch. für Pflanzenbau. *II:* 1-48

72 KAUTER, A., 1933. „Beiträge zur Kenntnis des Wurzelwachtums der Gräser." Ber. Schweiz. Bot. Ges. *42:* 37-108

73 KELLEY, O. J., J. A. HARDMAN and D. S. JENNINGS, 1947. „A soil sampling machine for obtaining two, three and four- inch diameter cores of undisturbed soil to a depth of six feet." Soil Sci. Soc. Amer. Proc. *12:* 85-87

74 KING, F. H., 1892. „Natural distribution of roots in field soils." Wis. Agric. Exp. Stat. *9th* Ann. Rep.: 112-120 and 1893, *10th* Ann. Rep.: 160-166

75 KLAPP, E., 1943. „Über die Wurzelverbreitung der Grasnarbe bei verschiedener Nutzungsweise und Pflanzengesellschaft." Pflanzenbau *19:* 221-236

76 KMOCH, H. G., 1952. „Über den Umfang und einige Gesetzmäszigkeiten der Wurzelmassenbildung unter Grasnarben." Z.f. Acker-u. Pfl. bau. *95:* 363-380

77 KMOCH, H. G., 1960. „Die Herstellung von Wurzelprofilen mit Hilfe des UTAH-Erdbohrers und ihre Ausdeutung. 1. Mitt. Methodik von Wurzel-Profil-Herstellung." Z.f. Acker-u. Pfl. bau *110:* 249-254

78 KMOCH, H. G., 1960. „Die Herstellung von Wurzelprofilen mit Hilfe des UTAH-Erdbohrers und ihre Ausdeutung." 2. Mitt. Z. f. Acker-u. Pfl. bau *110:* 425-437

79 KMOCH, H. G., 1961. „Idem. 3. Mitt." Z. f. Acker-u. Pfl. bau *113:* 342-360

80 KÖHNLEIN, J. und H. VETTER, 1953. „Ernterückstände und Wurzelbild." Paul Parey, Berlin, 138 pp.

81 KÖNEKAMP, A., 1953. „Teilergebnisse von Wurzeluntersuchungen." Z. f. Pfl. ern. D. u. Bodk. *60:* 113-124

82 KÖNEKAMP, A. und F. KÖNIG, 1929. „Bericht über die Tätigkeit des Instituts für Grünlandwirtschaft." Landwirtsch. Jahrb. Ergänzungsband *69:* 208-225

83 KRAUS, C., 1888. ,,Das Wurzelsystem der Runkelrüben und dessen Beziehungen zur Rübenkultur." Wollney: Agrikulturphysik *11:* 358-406

84 KRAUS, C., 1911. ,,Untersuchungen zu den biologischen Grundlagen des Grasbaues." Fühl. Landwirtsch. Ztg. *60:* 329-345 und 377-401

85 KULESCHA, M., 1931. ,,Oriënterend onderzoek over de ontwikkeling van het wortelstelsel bij 2878 P.O.J. in verband met de grondsoort." Meded. Proefst. Java suikerind. *8:* 317-359

86 KVARAZKHELIA, T. K., 1931. ,,Beiträge zur Biologie des Wurzelsystemes der Obstbäume." Gartenbau-wiss. *4:* 239-241

87 LAIRD, A. S., 1930. ,,A study of the root systems of some important sod-forming grasses." Florida Agric. Exp. Stat. Bull. *211*

88 LAMBA, P. S., H. L. AHLGREN and R. J. MUCKENHIRN, 1949. ,,Root growth of alfalfa, medium red clover, brome grass and timothy under various soil conditions." Agron. J. *41:* 451-458

89 LIESHOUT, J. W. van, 1955. ,,Bepaling der wortelactiviteit met behulp van radioactieve isotopen." De plantenwortel in de landbouw: 199-204

90 LIESHOUT, J. W. van, 1956. ,,De beworteling van een aantal landbouw-gewassen." Versl. Landbk. Onderz. *62*, 46 pp.

91 LIESHOUT, J. W. van, 1957. ,,De invloed van de wortelontwikkeling op de waterhuishouding van een hoge zandgrond." Landbk. T. *69:* 165-179

92 LINKOLA, K. und A. TIIRIKKA, 1936. ,,Über Wurzelsysteme und Wur-zelausbreitung der Wiesenpflanzen auf verschiedenen Wiesen-standorten." Helsinki, 207 pp.

93 LOW, A. J., 1951. ,,The use of isotopes in agricultural researchII." Chem. and Ind.: 1124-1128

94 MASCHHAUPT, J. G., 1911. ,,Reactieverandering van de bodem ten gevolge van plantengroei en bemesting." Versl. Landbk. Onderz. *10:* 50-93

95 MASCHHAUPT, J. G., 1915. ,,De beworteling onzer cultuurgewassen." Versl. Landbouwk. Onderz. *16:* 76-89

96 MASCHHAUPT, J. G., 1916. ,,Over antagonistische werkingen van zouten bij planten." Versl. Landbk. Onderz. *19*, 60 pp.

97 METSÄVAINIO, K., 1931. ,,Untersuchungen über das Wurzelsystem der Moorpflanzen." Helsinki

98 MEYERS, P. G. en M. A. J. GOEDEWAAGEN, 1936. ,,Een onderzoek naar de beworteling van lucerne." Versl. Landbk. Onderz. *42:* 649-667

99 MIELCK, O., 1913. ,,Die Wirkungen der Gründüngung." Fühl. Landwirtsch. Ztg. *62:* 585

100 NAD'JARANYI, F. M., 1939. ,,Some data on the study of root systems and plant mixtures." Sowet. Agron. *5:* 49-57

101 NAJMR, S., 1957. ,,Über die Methode der Isolierung der Wurzelsysteme der Futterpflanzen aus dem Boden." Z. f. Acker-u. Pfl. bau. *104:* 103-109

102 NOBBE, F., 1862. ,,Über die feinere Verästelung der Pflanzenwurzel." Die Landwirtsch. Versuchsstat. *4:* 212-224

103 NOBBE, F., 1875. ,,Beobachtungen und Versuche über die Wurzelbildung der Nadelhölzer." Die Landwirtsch. Versuchsstat. *18:* 279-295

104 NUTMAN, F. J., 1934. ,,The root system of coffea arabica." The Emp. J. Exp. Agric., *2:* 293-302

105 OBERMAYER, E., 1939. ,,Root study technique." Herb. Rev. *7:* 175

106 OSKAMP, J. and L. P. BATJER, 1933. ,,Soils in relation to fruit growing in New York. III. Some physical and chemical properties of the soils of the Hilton and Morton Areas, Monroe County and their relation to orchard performance." Cornell Univ. Agric. Exp. Stat. Bull. *575:* 1-34

107 OSVALD, H., 1919. ,,Untersuchungen über die Einwirking des Grundwasserstands auf die Bewurzelung von Wiesenpflanzen auf Moorböden." Fühl. Landwirtsch. Ztg. *68:* 321 und 370

108 PAVLYCHENKO, T. K., 1937. ,,Quantitative study of the entire root systems of weed and crop plants under field conditions." Ecology *18:* 62-79

109 PAVLYCHENKO, T. K., 1937. ,,The soil-block washing method in quantitative root study." Canad. J. Res. C. *15:* 33-57

110 RAPPAPORT, J., 1938. ,,Onderzoekingen over de ontwikkeling der wortels bij Lolium perenne L." Meded. Landbouwhogeschool Gent *VI:* 120-204

111 RATAJ, R. und I. LIEBEROTH, 1957. ,,Über die Entnahme von Bodenproben in natürlicher Lagerung." Z. f. Pfl. ern. D. u. Bodk. *77:* 52-58

112 RICHARDSON, S. D., 1956. ,,Photosynthesis and root growth in tree seedlings." Landbk. T. *68:* 775-783

113 ROBERTS, R. A. and I. V. HUNT, 1936. ,,The effect of shoot cutting on the growth of root and shoot of perennial ryegrass and timothy." Welsh. J. Agric. *12:* 158-174

114 ROGERS, W. S., 1939/40. ,,Root studies. IX. The effect of light on growing apple roots. A trial with root observation boxes." J. Pomol. and Hort. Sci. *17:* 131-140

115 ROO, H. C. de, 1957. ,,Root growth in Connecticut tobacco soils." Conn. Agric. Exp. Stat. Bull. *608*, 36 pp.

116 ROTMISTROFF, W. G., 1907. ,,Die Gebiete der Verbreitung der Wurzeln bei einjährigen Kulturpflanzen." Russ. J. F. Exp. Landwirt. *VIII:* 530

117 ROTMISTROFF, W. G., 1908. ,,Idem, Fortsetzung." Russ. J. f. Exp. Landwirt. *IX:* 1-26

118 ROTMISTROFF, W. G., 1926. ,,Das Wesen der Dürre, ihre Ursache und Verhütung." Ubersetzt von Ernst van Riesen

119 SACHS, J., 1860. ,,Bericht über die physiologische Thätigkeit an der Versuchsstation in Tharandt." Die Landwirtsch. Versuchsstat. *2:* 167 und 219

120 SCHULZ, W., 1958. ,,Einige Beobachtungen über kurzfristige Veränderungen im Boden auf kleinstem Raum." Z.f. Pfl. ern. D. u. Bodk. *80* (125): 66

121 SCHULZE, B., 1911. ,,Wurzelatlas I" Paul Parey, Berlin

122 SCHULZE, B., 1914. ,,Wurzelatlas II" Paul Parey, Berlin

123 SCHUURMAN, J. J., 1947. ,,Vergelijking van twee methoden van wortelonderzoek." Verslag

124 SCHUURMAN, J. J., 1949. ,,Vergelijking van de resultaten van een bemonstering op weiland met boren van verschillende diameter." Verslag

125 SCHUURMAN, J. J., 1949. ,,Voorbereidend wortelonderzoek in verband met humusbepalingen in weiland." Verslag

126 SCHUURMAN, J. J. en M. A. J. GOEDEWAAGEN, 1949. ,,Werkschema voor het personeel in de spoelafdeling van wortelmonsters." Niet gepubliceerd

127 SCHUURMAN, J. J. and M. A. J. GOEDEWAAGEN, 1955. ,,A new method for the simultaneous preservation of profiles and root systems." Plant and Soil *6:* 373-381

128 SCHUURMAN, J. J. en L. KNOT, 1957. ,,Het schatten van hoeveelheden wortels in voor wortelonderzoek genomen monsters." Versl. Landbk. Onderz. *63.* 14, 31 pp

129 SCHWENDIMAN, J. L., A. L. HAFENRICHTER and A. G. LAW, 1953. ,,The production of tops and roots by grass and sweet clover when grown in mixtures." Agron. J. *45:* 110-114

130 SEELHORST, C. von, 1902. ,,Beobachtungen über die Zahl und den Tiefgang der Wurzeln verschiedener Pflanzen bei verschiedener Düngung des Bodens." J. für Landwirtschaft *50:* 91-104

131 SIMON, W. und D. EICH, 1955. ,,Probleme und Methoden der Wurzeluntersuchungen (unter besonderer Berücksichtigung leichterer Böden)." Z. f. Acker-u. Pfl. bau *100:* 179-198

132 SLËSKIN, P., 1908. ,,Werden Nitrate von den Wurzeln assimiliert oder nicht?" Russ. J. f. Exp. Landwirt. *IX:* 32

133 SMITH, A. J. and L. A. MABBITT, 1953. ,,The contribution to soil organic matter and nitrogen from cereal residues and undersown crops." The J. of Soil Sci. *4:* 98-105

134 SOLBERG, P., 1935. ,,Untersuchungen über die Wurzelausscheidungen verschiedener Pflanzen bei ihrer Kultur ohne und mit Zusatz von Nährsalzen." Landwirtsch. Jahrb. *81:* 891-917

135 SPRAGUE, H. B., 1933. ,,Root development of perennial grasses and its relations to soil conditions." Soil Sci. *36:* 189-209

136 STOECHELER, J. H. and W. A. KLUENDER, 1938. ,,The hydraulic method of excavating the root systems of plants." Ecology *19:* 355-369

137 STUCKEY, J. H., 1941. ,,Seasonal growth of grass roots." Amer. J. Bot. *28:* 486-491

138 THAMES, J. L. and R. D. REYNOLDS, 1961. ,,A hydraulic soil sampler." Agric. Engin. *42:* 431-432

139 THIEL, H., 1892/3. ,,Anleitung zu Wurzelstudien." Mitt. d. Deutschen Landwirtsch. Ges. *7:* 75-76

140 TOLLENAAR, D., 1930. ,,Onderzoekingen over de ontwikkeling van het wortelstelsel van tabak onder verschillende omstandigheden; tevens bezien in verband met cultuurmaatregelen en brandbaarheid." Meded. Proefstat. Vorstl. Tabak. *65*

141 TROUGHTON, A., 1951. ,,Studies on the roots and storage organs of herbage plants." J. Brit. Grassl. Soc., *6:* 197-206

142 TUCKER, M. und C. VON SEELHORST, 1898. ,,Der Einfluss, welchen der Wassergehalt und der Reichtum des Bodens auf die Ausbildung der Wurzeln und der oberirdischen Organe der Haferpflanzen ausüben." J. für Landwirtschaft *46:* 52-63

143 UPCHURCH, R. P., 1951. ,,The use of trench-wash and soil-elution methods for studying alfalfa roots." Agron. J. *43:* 552-555

144 WATENPAUGH, H. N., 1936. ,,The influence of the reaction of soil strata upon the root development of alfalfa. Soil Sci. *41:* 449-467

145 WEAVER, J. E., 1926. ,,Root development of field crops." Mc Graw Hill Book Co. Inc. New York, 291 pp.

146 WEAVER, J. E. and R. W. DARLAND, 1947. ,,A method of measuring vigor of range grasses." Ecology *28:* 146-161

147 WEAVER, J. E. , J. KRAMER and M. REED, 1924. ,,Development of roots and shoots of winter wheat under field environment." Ecology *5:* 26-50

148 WEAVER, J. E. and J. W. VOIGT, 1950. ,,Monolith method of root-sampling in studies on succession and degeneration." Bot. Gaz. *111:* 286-299

149 WEAVER, J. E. and ELLEN ZINK, 1946. ,,Length of life of roots of ten species of perennial range and pasture grasses." Plant Physiol. *21:* 201-217

150 WETTE, W., 1942. ,,Über die Wirkung verschiedener Schnitthäufigkeit auf Eiweissleistung, Ausdauer und Wurzelentwicklung sowie Nährstoffentzug und Düngungsbedürfnis der Luzerne." Landwirtsch. Jahrb. *91:* 941-982

151 WETZEL, M., 1958. ,,Der Futterroggen, die Futterroggengemische und die sonstige Futtergemische des Winterzwischenfutterbaues als Lieferanten von Futter und Wurzeln." Wissensch. Z. Univ. Rostock: 89-366

152 WILLARD, C. J. and G. M. MC CLURE, 1932. ,,The quantitative development of tops and roots in blue grass with an improved method of obtaining root yields." J. Amer. Soc. Agron. *24*: 509-514

153 WILLIAMS, F. E. and H. K. BAKER, 1957. ,,Studies on the root development of herbage plants. 1. Techniques of herbage root investigations." J. Brit. Grassl. Soc. *12*: 49-55

154 WITTE, K., 1929. ,,Beitrag zu den Grundlagen des Grasbaus." Landwirtsch. Jahrb. *69*: 253

155 WORZELLA, W. W., 1932. ,,Root development in hardy and non hardy winter wheat varieties." J. Amer. Soc. Agron. *24*: 626-637

156 WIJK, W. R. van, 1952. ,,De bepaling van de werkzaamheid der wortels met behulp van radio-actieve isotopen." Landbk. T. *64*: 398-399

157 YODER, R. E., 1936. ,,A direct method of aggregate analysis of soils and a study of the physical nature of erosion losses." J. Amer. Soc. Agron. *28*: 337-351

158 ZIJLSTRA, K., 1922. ,,De hoofdwortel van enige graansoorten." Versl. Landbk. Onderz. *26*: 19-59

Key to the bibliography

Field experiments

Investigations of monolithes
a. the pinboard method: 4, 47, 50, 70, 90, 91, 92, 95, 97, 108, 109, 110, 115, 117, 127, 151.
b. excavations: 17, 22, 33, 39, 41, 42, 54, 55, 63, 64, 67, 74, 84, 108, 109, 116, 137, 143, 146, 148, 151, 152.

Investigations of soil specimens
a. the auger method: 1, 2, 3, 11, 14, 19, 21, 31, 44, 45, 50, 51, 58, 60, 68, 69, 73, 75, 76, 77, 78, 79, 81, 87, 100, 111, 115, 118, 123, 124, 125, 126, 128, 129, 130, 131, 133, 138, 141, 151, 153, 157.
b. other methods: 13, 38, 80, 81, 92, 98, 129, 135, 143, 154.

Investigations of profile walls
a. mapping out, followed by counting: 20, 21, 106.
b. preparing of roots in situ: 12, 16, 17, 27, 30, 32, 37, 57, 58, 67, 72, 84, 85, 86, 92, 97, 99, 104, 115, 116, 136, 139, 140, 143, 145, 154, 155.
c. other methods: 10, 22, 54, 80, 97, 99, 116, 139.

Container experiments

Cylinder experiments: 15, 24, 26, 35, 46, 47, 147, 149, 150.
Experiments in boxes and cases
a. general: 5, 15, 24, 26, 36, 47, 48, 49, 56, 59, 65, 71, 82, 83, 84, 95, 105, 107, 113, 117, 118, 121, 122, 144, 146, 150.
b. roots behind a glass panel: 6, 10, 25, 49, 53, 63, 66, 72, 82, 112, 114, 120, 134.

Pot cultures: 7, 9, 17, 23, 28, 40, 53, 61, 63, 65, 71, 83, 84, 88, 94, 102, 103, 110, 130, 132, 142, 158.

Water cultures: 18, 23, 28, 29, 34, 43, 62, 96, 110, 119, 158.

Isotopes: 8, 89, 93, 156.